WHITWORTH

For over 40 years, "Whitworth" cartoons appeared in Sheffield's newspapers. During this time he became a daily fixture in the city's life - targeting both the serious and the absurd issues of the day with an unerring eye.

Over these years, while Prime Ministers, local councillors, football managers and celebrities came and went, Whitworth's cartoons were a consistent presence on the newspapers' front pages. From unemployment and the state of the economy to potholes and the mysteries of town planning departments, via the trials and tribulations of local football teams and their long-suffering supporters, Whitworth captured the mood of his time.

The former Home Secretary, David Blunkett - himself frequently a target for the cartoonist - called Whitworth a "Sheffield Institution". He has been quoted as an inspiration for a new generation of cartoonists, including Sheffield's own McKee; and to this day, his cartoons hang in offices and boardrooms from Yorkshire to London and beyond.

Despite the many awards and accolades he received throughout his career (including lifetime membership of the Playboy club - something his wife suggested he might not want to take up), Whitworth the man remained essentially the same: modest, compassionate and very, very funny.

The cartoons included here date mainly from the 1990s. They range from political satire and trenchant observational humour through to groan-worthy puns. They cover a wide number of topics, including local and national government, sport, the Student Games and Supertram (both godsends to a cartoonist) and of course - the weather. They remain as pertinent now as the day they first appeared.

Whitworth's cartoons made thousands laugh on a daily basis for over four decades. Now with this new collection, there is the opportunity for them to do so again.

Acknowledgements:
Thanks to Alan Powell, editor of the Sheffield Star, for kind permission to reproduce the cartoons.
Also to Peter Kay of the Sheffield Telegraph for the initial suggestion.

For Lois Whitworth

Education, or the lack of it

supertram, more teething problems

I waited for ages for a reply from the Department of Transport, then two came

Town Planning, or not

"You mean the city centre was PLANNED to look like this?"

Euro '96 Championship,
The Danish beerfest departs

When the wind's in the right direction
you can hear all Sheffield landlords
sobbing goodbye to the Danes

Education, or the lack of it

Standards are improving - our teacher can spell better than some of the pupils

New Labour -
happy days?

Football, Wednesday's new training methods

I've been roughing it on these moors for years and I'm STILL no good at football

Whitworth
illustrated by a colleague

WHITWORTH

Whitworth by Harvey.

This is a drawing of Whitworth
by Peter Harvey. He exercised his artistic
licence and tidied Whitworth's hair a little.

sheffielders, the odd moan

We should tell Sheffielders what it's going to cost NOW - while they're still in a good mood

I want to hear Peak National Park boasting of having Sheffield on its doorstep

sheffield Airport, it went soon after Saddam

Slight mix-up at Tinsley - I wanted a flight to Amsterdam and they thought I said a flight to slam Saddam

Transferred, not too big a move

Whitworth's last cartoon for the
Morning Telegraph, February 8th, 1986,
and his first for the
Sheffield Telegraph

sheffield's own
astronaut,
did she enjoy
the trip?

WHITWORTH

They took her to their leader

Maternity Hospitals,
now just Jessops

I was made redundant -
I used to do the Nether Edge Hospital flight

Libraries, quality of books

Filthy, smelly hands - you've been playing with my library books again

World student Games 1991
not really a
media frenzy

Doris - I think I've spotted some coverage of
the Student Games in the national press

Student Games did tha gu to see owt int Arena?

It's not the English they're going to have problems with, it's Sheffieldish

Television influence on some children

I worry about him - he doesn't like
Teenage Mutant Ninja Turtles

Close encounters in south Yorkshire

I've never seen a Martian but I once saw a woman in Cudworth's West End Club

sheffield Wednesday, 1976
dark days around
Hillsborough

Football, Frogmarched through sheffield

...and there's the Cantona Way -
France to Leeds, via Hillsborough

Football,
Big Ron's return

One black curly wig, one false beard and one false nose for August 17th - yes, Mr Atkinson

Wolrd snooker Championship, on cue for charity

WHITWORTH

Somebody suggested a snooker stars' charity soccer match but they'd want the ball cleaning every time they got a kick

sheffield United,
at last a premiership ground

WHITWORTH

Are you sitting
comfortably?
Good, then we'll begin

Poor Architecture?

"It splits the city in half, like that Manpower Services building at the bottom of the Moor."

Environment, then and now

"Grandad liked Sheffield better when it had dirty air and clean streets."

Public Convenience, a motion passed

FACELIFT FOR TOWN HALL PUBLIC TOILETS

"Not before time - there's graffiti down there saying 'Stop Hitler and Mussolini now'."

Parking, a fine mess

"Or if you live in Sheffield, we'll pay your first three weeks' parking charges."

Rules and Regulations, we must obey?

"Of COURSE you feel persecuted - you smoke, you drink beer and you park your car in Sheffield."

High street, during the supertram installation

"Actually we live in Leeds but come to Sheffield every week for the closing down sales."

Election time, blowing hot, but mostly cold

"It beats me why it's still so cold after four
weeks of constant hot air."

"...then we encounter some really gruelling terrain - Fargate and the Moor."

Police Brutality, as seen by football fans

"I thought I'd practice being courteous
and kind to football fans and he fainted."

Michael Jackson's visit to Don Valley

"I was a bit disappointed - no Jarvis Cocker!"

The retail world, swings and roundabouts

"The good news is that city centre shoplifters have deserted us for Meadowhall"

Real Ale, real truth?

supertram, belief was all that was needed!

"...and thank you for Sheffield for getting a Bishop
who believes in God, the Bible and Supertram"

sports centres, replacing houses, shops, industry?

supertram, plenty of parking, not much riding

"That was a bit of a let down
I thought it said Bark and Ride"

centre for popular music, a white elephant?

"Coach party from Sheffield - stand by
for a spate of white elephant jokes"

Our Rights, or how the legal system cashes in

"I'm bottom of the class in the bottom
school - there must be SOMEBODY
I can sue"

Education, more leisure time needed?

"Oh, not another student giving
up university because there's no pyjama jump"

"It still sounds to me as if Midland Mainline are saying people can't get out of Sheffield quick enough"

Road Tax, or highway robbery

"Don't be silly - they wouldn't dig up the whole street just to stop us using our car"

Botany, or leaf the money to us

"That should buy us a few leaves to turn over"

Attercliffe Nightspot, or shortlived advert?

"Oh, look, Fred - cigarette advertising is back!"

Libraries, help needed

"It's for a good cause - they pass them on to Sheffield's needy public libraries"

TV Coverage,
or the lack of it

TOO MUCH STUDENT GAMES ON TV

"Probably comes from Leeds"

sheaf fragrance, not as good as Pond's

The Blades, the usual story

"Sheffield United?
bottom of the top table"

Blades, army training, for a rearguard action?

"Instead of running out from the tunnel they'll probably abseil down from the floodlights"

stadium, ameneties on tap

"That £100,000 storm water sewer is going to be a big drain on our resources"

Education, could do with a lift

Music, money for nothing

"...and before you start going on about the Student Games, it's a pop group"

Armoury, one in the eye for sheffield

"Harold's got this terrible premonition that our armour will finish up in Leeds instead of Sheffield"

sheffield school, nothing changes

"We're holding it early before
the council close us"

The Blades, happier days

"I want to sue Brian Deane for ruining all my Sheffield United jokes"

Gulf War, shopping or shooting

"I'm from Sheffield - all MY wife writes about is Meadowhall"

Football getting to the bottom of it

"I think that's carrying the all-seater stadium idea a bit far"

Highways, becoming dated

Sporting Events, can we cope with another?

"Is my husband well enough to be told that Sheffield is bidding for another sporting extravaganza, Doctor"

Canal, can anyone navigate this scheme

"There was a time when I wouldn't have touched it with a barge pole"

Good Ideas?

"It's a wheel
my other great idea is a poll tax"

Parking, everything is cheaper at Meadowhall

"That's not much help -
the city centre's miles from Meadowhall"

United, they always keep us laughing

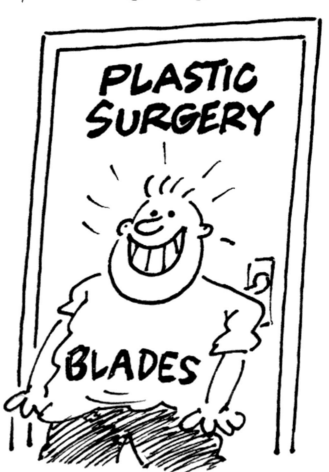

Regulations, falling in line with the council

"I fell off a pile of new safety regulations"

Winter roads, or a pinch of salt for luck!

"You should be like Sheffield Highways
Department and cut down on salt"

Water, Water, everywhere, not a drop to spare

"Another Drink of water? Your mother and I aren't MADE of money you know"

Owls, still going to the dogs?

"Mine's called Wednesday -
he can't hold a lead"

Education, more heads than the hydra

Speaking of Rudyard Kipling, Miss, it's a pity we're losing our head
when all about are keeping theirs

Cricket, e's from Manchseter, it shunt be allowed

"I'm not watching a Yorkshire team with Lancastrians in it!"

Cartoonist at work, thinking funny

HERE ARE THE NEWS HEADLINES — WAR... RAIL DISASTER... MURDER... PLANE CRASH — EARTHQUAKE... RIOT DEATHS...

THINK FUNNY

Here's how Ralph Whitworth sees himself